ELSTON©

ELSTON ON ICE

POLESTAR

BOOK PUBLISHERS

Published by
Polestar Press Ltd., #3–373 Baker Street, Nelson, B.C., V1L 4H6 (604) 354-4482

Distributed by
Raincoast Books, 112 East 3rd Avenue, Vancouver, B.C., V5T 1C8 (604) 873-6581

Canadian Cataloguing in Publication Data
Elston, Dave, 1958-
Elston on ice

ISBN 0-919591-59-0

1. Hockey—Caricatures and cartoons.
2. Canadian wit and humor, Pictorial. I. Title.
NC1449.E48A4 1990   741.5'971   C90-091586-2

Acknowledgements
Never mind the book–if it weren't for these people I wouldn't even be cartooning!!

Bill Davidson
Pat Doyle
Russ Farwell
The Grahams
Bob McKenzie
Rod McLeod
Nan & Laurie
Al Ruckaber
John Shannon
...and all my buddies who are sick of hearing "I can't–I've gotta work tonight!"

THANKS

These cartoons previously appeared in the *Calgary Sun, Edmonton Sun,*
The Hockey News, or *Inside Hockey.*

Printed in Canada

CONTENTS

This collection of cartoons is dedicated to MAW.

NIGHTMARES

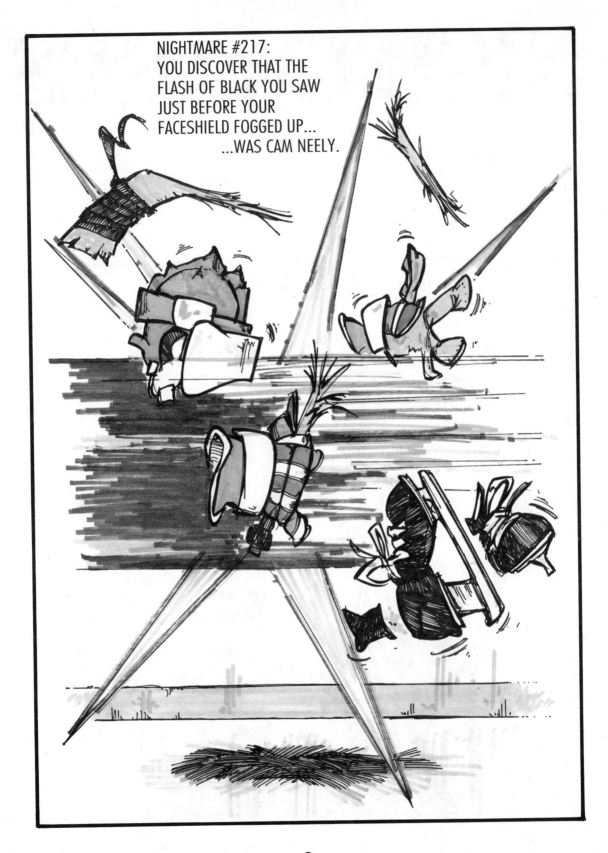

NIGHTMARE #143:
WHILE SKATING PAST DAVE
BROWN, YOUR GLOVES
ACCIDENTALLY FALL OFF.

NIGHTMARE #152:
YOU CUT DOWN TIM HUNTER
WITH A VICIOUS TWO-
HANDER...

...AND HE GETS BACK UP.

NIGHTMARE #491:
YOU GIVE YOUR OFFICIATING PARTNER THE SIGNAL THAT IT'S TIME TO BREAK UP THE JAY MILLER - DAVE BROWN SCRAP...

...AND HE MISSES IT.

NIGHTMARE #732:
YOU MEET THE PLAYBOY
PLAYMATE OF THE YEAR...

...5 MINUTES AFTER YOUR
ROOKIE INITIATION.

NIGHTMARE #429:
YOU'RE SO INTIMIDATED
FACING OFF AGAINST STEVE
KASPER THAT YOU GET
TOSSED OUT...

...OF A CEREMONIAL FACEOFF.

NIGHTMARE #888:
YOU'RE THE TRAINER WHO
HAS TO DECIDE IF CLAUDE
LEMIEUX IS ACTUALLY
INJURED.

1989-90 REGULAR SEASON

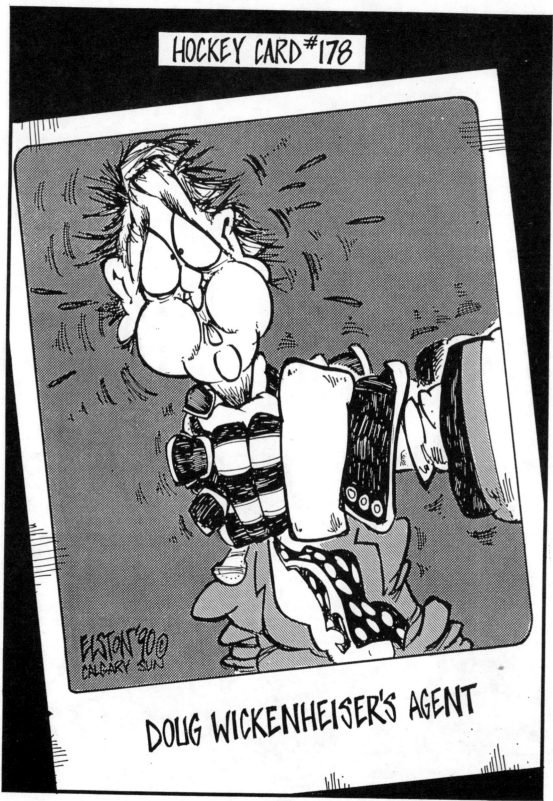

DOUG WICKENHEISER LOWEST PAID PLAYER IN NHL

TRI-CITY AMERICANS' TEAM PICTURE

TOP ROW: (LEFT TO RIGHT) BILL LaFORGE

DECEMBER 1989 — THE
TRI-CITY AMERICANS WALK-
OUT ON THEIR NEWLY
APPOINTED COACH.

HALLOWEEN 1989 — JIM PEPLINSKI RETIRES.

AFTER DEMANDING TO BE TRADED, JIMMY CARSON FINALLY GETS HIS WISH.

1990 PLAYOFFS

THE SIMPSONS

HOMER

BART

CRAIG

CALGARY FINDS SIMILARITIES
IN L.A.'S STYLE OF PLAY.

BASEBALL SEASON BEGINS.

MAY, 1990 — TERRY CRISP FIRED

EDMONTON VS. L.A. — THE KINGS GO DOWN 3 GAMES TO NONE.

GRETZKY, PLAGUED BY A BAD BACK, IS LISTED AS A DOUBTFUL STARTER.

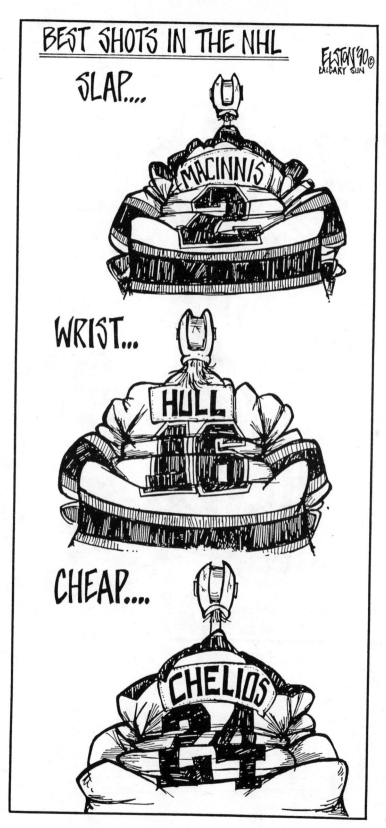

CHRIS CHELIOS
RUNS OVER
ANDY MOOG.

THE MIKE KEENAN DREAM TEAM

A CARTOON FROM INSIDE CHICAGO STADIUM

BOSTON GARDEN

THE OILERS FAIL TO SWEEP BOSTON.

TOUGH GUYS

DAVE BROWN

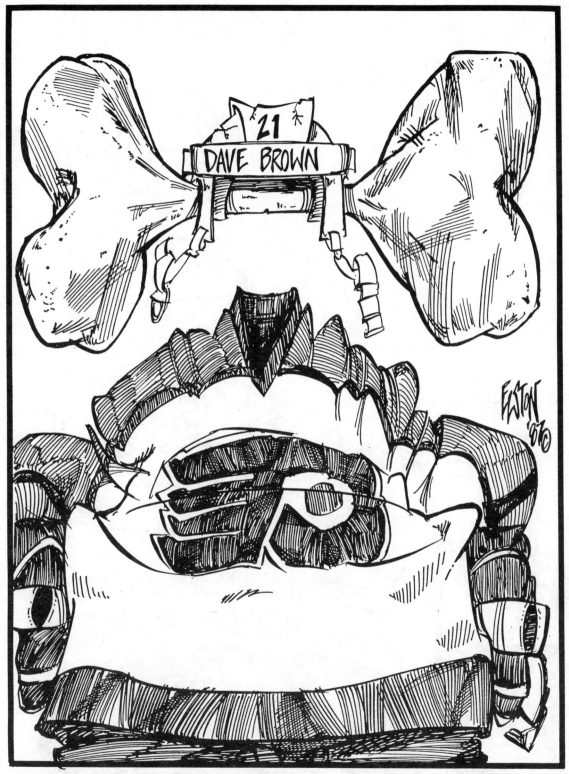

1987 — FOLLOWING DAVE'S VICIOUS CROSS-CHECK ON TOMAS SANDSTROM.

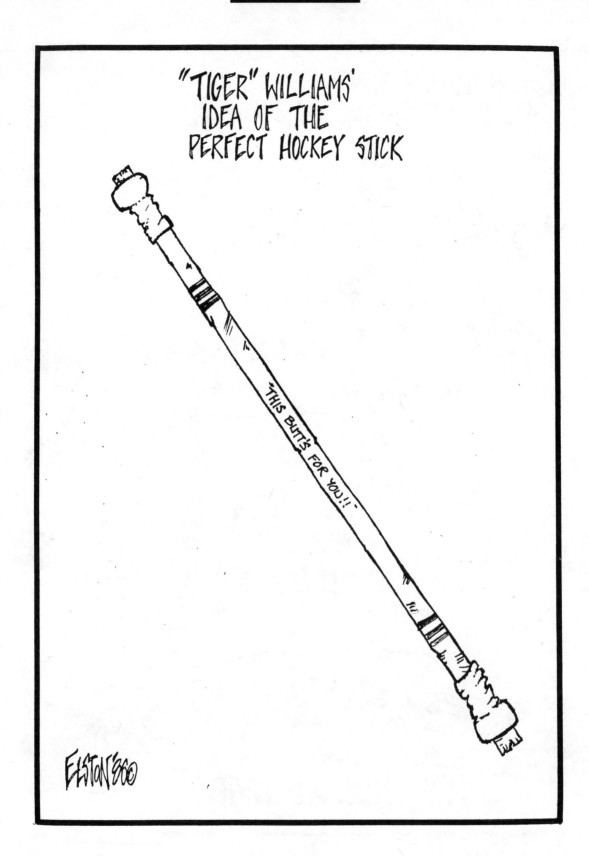

Reducing the number of injuries in the N.H.L.

TIGER WILLIAMS

MARTY McSORLEY

PLAYOFFS 1988 — MCSORLEY CLAIMS HE WAS IN A FOG FROM A HARD HIT
WHEN HE SPEARED CALGARY'S MIKE BULLARD.

GRETZKY

L.A. COACH, ROBBIE FTOREK, SAYS GRETZKY'S JUST ONE OF TWENTY PLAYERS ON THE TEAM.

WAYNE AND DAVE SEMENKO

CALGARY FANS DUB GRETZKY "THE WHINER."

GRETZKY'S VERSION
OF THE PERFECT AIRPLANE

FLAMES TOUGH GUY, NEIL SHEEHY, IS A CONSTANT SOURCE OF AGGRAVATION.

THE WEDDING

THE TUCK-XEDO

KEVIN McCLELLAND, UNAWARE THAT THROWING RICE IS A FRIENDLY GESTURE

THE WEDDING DANCE

MARK MESSIER CATCHES THE GARTER

THE HONEYMOON

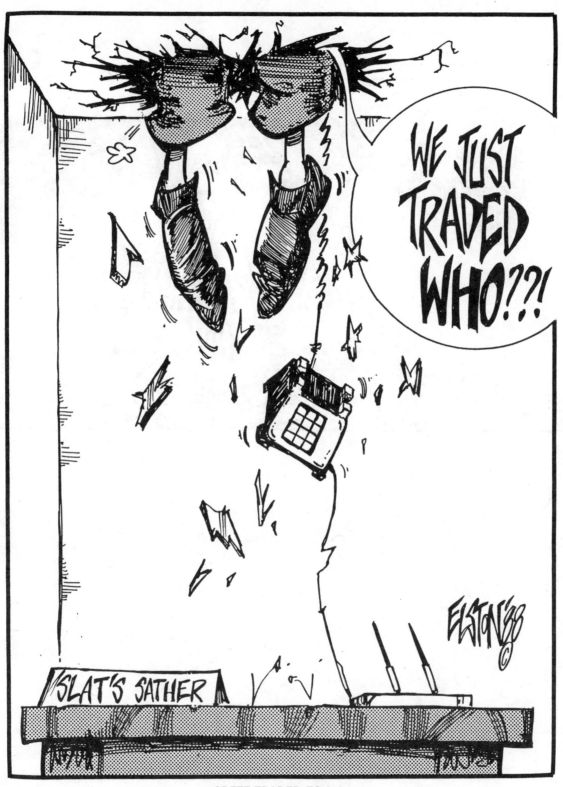

GRETZ TRADED TO L.A.

MAHATMA GRETZKY

THE GREAT ONE CALLS FOR A
BAN ON FIGHTING.

AS THE LEAGUE TURNS

FLAMES SIGN SOVIET, SERGEI PRIAKIN.

THE CAVITY-FIGHTER

OCTOBER 1988 — RICH SUTTER LOSES SEVERAL TEETH COURTESY OF MARK MESSIER.

CALGARY - ST. LOUIS TRADES BECOME A REGULAR OCCURRENCE.

PLAYOFFS 1989 — CALGARY BARELY SQUEAKS BY THE CANUCKS IN THE FIRST ROUND.

PLAYOFFS 1988 — DURING AN OFF-ICE SHOUTING MATCH, DEVIL'S COACH JIM SCHOENFELD TELLS REFEREE DON KOHARSKI TO "HAVE ANOTHER DONUT YOU FAT PIG!!"

THE BATTLE OF ALBERTA??

HALLOWEEN 1988

THE '80'S — A TOUGH DECADE ON THE LEAFS.

PLAYOFFS, 1989 — FLAMES TRAINER, "BEARCAT" MURRAY, RUSHES ONTO THE ICE TO ATTEND A FALLEN PLAYER... WHILE THE PLAY'S STILL ON.

ELSTON '85

31 PELLE LINDBERGH

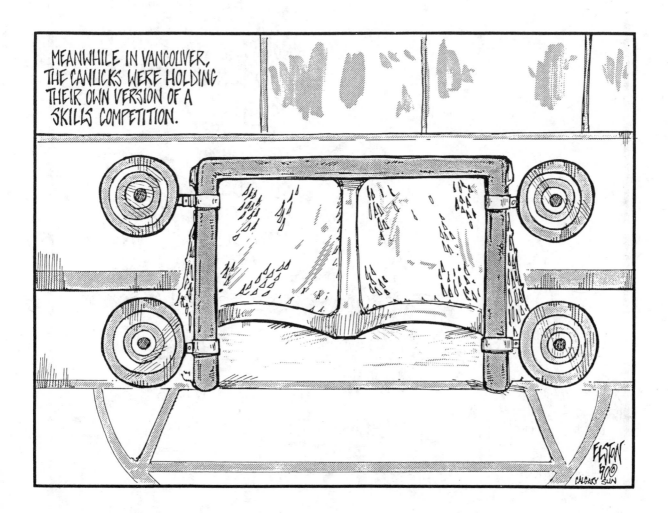

KEN LINSEMAN BITES LEE FOGOLIN IN A FIGHT.

EDMONTON OILERS' STEVE SMITH

CZECH TEEN-AGER PETR NEDVED DEFECTS FROM A CALGARY MIDGET HOCKEY TOURNAMENT.

Q: IF WINNIPEG JETS' DEFENCEMAN, RANDY CARLYLE, CHANGED HIS NUMBER TO 767, WHAT WOULD HE BECOME?

A: WINNIPEG'S FIRST WIDE-BODY JET!

1984 — AN OVERWEIGHT RANDY CARLYLE

KENT NILSSON — NICKNAME: MAGIC (BECAUSE HE DISAPPEARS IN THE PLAYOFFS)

POLISH PLAYER TESTS POSITIVE FOR STEROIDS

HOCKEY CARD #121

HOCKEY NIGHT IN CANADA

DON CHERRY

DECEMBER 25, 1989 —
DON CHERRY MAKES THE
DRESSING FOR THE
CHRISTMAS TURKEY.

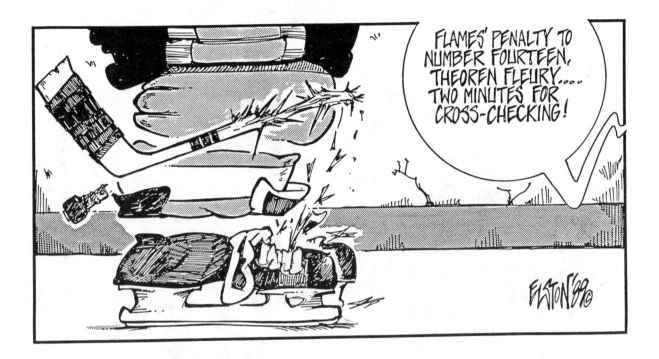